Blue

Revised, Edited,
Helped,
Inspired, and Loved

by Olivia and Luisa

Luli was a sweet, pretty little girl who loved the color blue.

She lived in her perfectly colorful world. Well, not so colorful…

She had everything she liked in her beautiful blue bedroom: charming blue dresses, fun blue toys, interesting blue books, and comfy blue shoes.

In the kitchen, it was not much different. Her mom prepared tasty blue grape juice for her, cooked healthy blue food, and then made her delicious desserts: blueberry pies!

Everywhere she looked and everything she touched all day long was blue! Luli's life was perfect, until she grew old enough to go to school.

School was not her favorite place. Everything and everyone was different, even her teacher. She wore a strange green dress one day, an okay yellow sweater the next, and sometimes she would come in not-so-fancy red pants, too!

Luli disliked red more than any other color. But, as shy as she was, she built the courage to ask her teacher a question.

"Why don't you ever wear blue?" she asked.

"Well, that's because I don't like blue that much, Luli! It makes me look pale. We all have our own favorite colors, don't we?", replied her teacher.

Luli couldn't understand why someone would think that blue would make them look pale.

Oh, and her classmates! One of them wore colorful clothes, and another one insisted in wearing flashy, old-fashioned pink sneakers. Pink! Argh!

She felt so lonely at school. She wished her mom could send her to one of those schools where kids wore uniforms. Blue uniforms, of course. Luli started a countdown calendar to summer break, when she would be able to go back to her perfect blue world.

FIRST DAY AT SCHOOL

But spring came and that was a time Luli dreaded. All of those blooming flowers, all of those colors. Why so many colors? And that field trip to the state park! Luli asked - begged, really – her mom to let her stay home, but mom was firm. "I have to go to work, and you should join your classmates in all of the class activities. A bit of fresh air will do you good!" she said.

When the dreadful day came, Luli was ready, well, as ready as one could be. Mom had made Luli's favorite blue corn bread (yes, such a thing as blue corn exists, and it is tasty, too!), a bottle of delicious grape juice, and some blueberry pudding as dessert. "Maybe this won't be so bad", thought Luli.

The trip started off well, but as she was getting off of the school bus, a disaster happened!

The day was grey, rainy, and a bit cold, and there was mud everywhere.

She stepped off of the bus on her tiptoes because she didn't want mud on her blue boots. But by doing so, she tripped and fell into the mud.

Her blue lunch box fell and flew open, and the food splashed everywhere in the mud. Now her clothes were wet and muddy, and she didn't have a lunch anymore.

Her day was turning out just as badly as she had feared. Even worse. She was hungry, wet, and cold.

Very wet, and very cold. Luli started crying.

Her friendly classmates felt bad for her.

A generous boy offered some of his fresh green edamame.

Another boy gave her some of his orange juice.

A nice little girl offered her a juicy green and pink mango.

And another kind girl gave her a red tomato.

Someone had an extra sweater, and she gave it to Luli.
It was yellow!!!!

Soon, everyone was helping her, and she had more than enough to eat and to get warm.

But...

None of it was blue. What was she going to do? What else could she do? She was cold and hungry, and she couldn't help but be grateful for all of her friends.

She started by eating the edamame.
"Hmmm, this doesn't taste that bad", she thought.

She was also very thirsty, so she drank her orange juice. "Nice", she thought. "A bit sweet, a bit bitter… tasty".

Her mango and tomato were sooo juicy, she ate them all up in seconds.

Finally, feeling much better already, she wore the yellow sweater, and guess what? It looked quite nice on her!

Next, the sun suddenly came out from behind the heavy clouds and shone on a field of wildflowers.

An explosion of colors and warmth cheered everyone up and warmed Luli too.

Suddenly, she was happy and able to appreciate the colorful flowers.

She had never played like she did that day. Everything was new to her; there were daisies, roses, bees, and trees.

She also began observing her new friends, their distinct voices, their hairstyles, their eyes and skin colors, and their contagious smiles. How rich and how alive it all felt!

Luli was always a very smart girl, and now she discovered how different people could be.

She started to pay more attention to the diversity of things: friendly brown dogs and charming grey cats, musical green birds and magical red dragonflies.

Sweet Luli quickly arrived at a conclusion: just like all of the animals in the world, humans are uniquely different, too.

Each and every one is special in their own way, unique in their own qualities and tastes. And, of course, not everyone had to like the color blue!

She also noticed that everyone is very similar: everybody needs love, care, attention, friends, food, and a home.

Luli no longer keeps a countdown calendar to summer, and she never daydreams of the school with the blue uniforms anymore.

She is thinking about wearing pink shoes or an orange sweater, and she certainly loves peaches, strawberries, oranges and other fruits.

She now likes edamame, and likes to try some new exotic vegetable from time to time, too!

Last week it was her birthday and a friend gave her a beautiful yellow handkerchief, which she decided to wear around her neck today. She thought it gives her blue dress quite a nice touch!

Summer vacations are just around the corner, and Luli is already making plans for it.

She wants to have play dates with her friends – even with John, who insists on only wearing his green dinosaur shirt.

She also wants to go to the park to play and to admire the flowers, and to try out the new set of crayons she asked for her birthday, with 60 different colors!

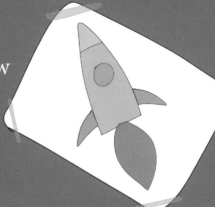